Wh

A game for
two or more players

by David Drew

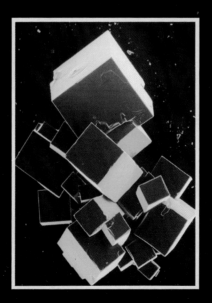

Most of the things in this book
can be found in your home
or your garden.

Use the pictures
and the clues
to work out the answers.

Cover the clues
with a piece of cardboard
and reveal them
one at a time.

It is about to disappear.
It was once in the sea.
It is wet.
It fell out of a cloud.
What is it?

It is part of an insect.
Each insect has two of them.
It is made of hundreds of lenses.
The insect is a fly.
What is it?

ANSWER: The eye of a fly.

Like many other insects, flies have compound eyes made of many
separate lenses. Human eyes have only one lens.

They are always with you.
They can be tiny, or
as long as your arm.
There are one hundred thousand
of them on your head.
What are they?

They are in your garden.
They are as small as pin heads.
You can find them under leaves.
Some of them are starting to hatch.
What are they?

ANSWER: Butterfly eggs.

Every kind of butterfly lays an egg with a different pattern on it.
You can see a caterpillar hatching out of one of the eggs.

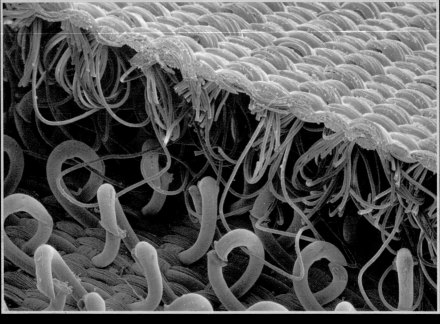

It is part of your clothes.
You also find it on space suits.
It is made of nylon.
It fastens and unfastens.
What is it?

It is part of an insect.
It has twelve black eyes.
It has prickles.
It chews a lot.
What is it?

ANSWER: The head of a caterpillar.

The eyes are the small black dots on each side of the head.
Only ten of them are visible in this picture.

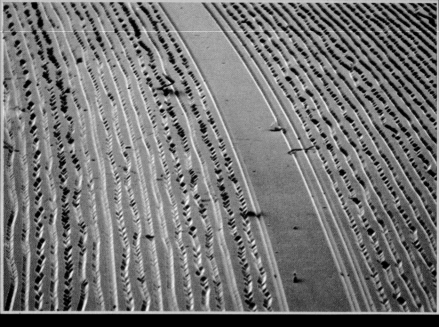

They go round in circles.
You keep them in your home.
A machine pressed them.
They make a lot of noise.
What are they?

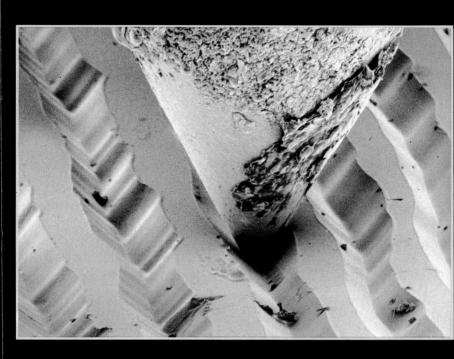

It is small and sharp.
Sometimes it vibrates.
It is made of diamond.
It produces music.
What is it?

ANSWER: A record needle.

The sloping sides of the groove make the needle vibrate.
The vibrations are turned into sound inside the speakers.
This needle has become very worn from too much playing.

They come from underground.
They are also found in the sea.
You use them in your kitchen.
You sprinkle them on your food.
What are they?

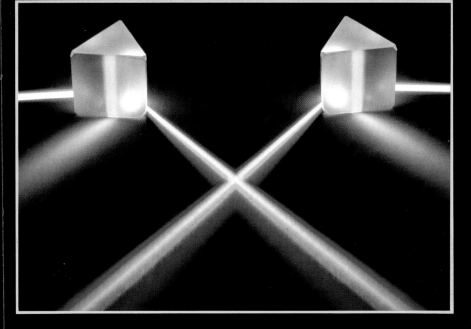

They are made of glass.
They are used in lasers.
They can bend rays of light.
They turn light into rainbows.
What are they?

ANSWER: Prisms.

White light is made of different colors. Each color is bent by the prism.
Red light is bent the most, and violet the least. The seven visible colors
in white light are red, orange, yellow, green, blue, indigo and violet.

13

It is a crystal.
It is found in orange juice
and in vegetables.
It helps prevent colds.
What is it?

ANSWER: Vitamin C.

Our bodies need vitamins to stay healthy. We get vitamins by eating
good food.

It lives on a beanstalk.
It sucks sap.
It is as big as a grain of salt.
It is a pest.
What is it?

ANSWER: Thrips.

Thrips are insects that feed in large groups on flowers and the new
stems of plants. The long spikes in the picture are hairs growing on
the bean leaf and on the beanstalk.

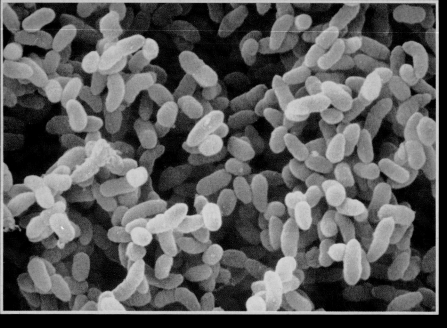

They live inside your body.
They are too small for you to see.
You don't like them.
They make you sick.
What are they?

ANSWER: Germs.

The germs in the picture are the bacteria that cause pneumonia.